True Stories of Animal Heroes

Fluffles

True Stories of Animal Heroes

Fluffles

Vita Murrow

Rachel Qiuqi

Frances Lincoln
Children's Books

Fluffles the koala lived in a eucalyptus forest.
It stretched across south-eastern Australia.
Fluffles' home was filled with tasty trees,
and many other friendly koalas.

Fluffles filled her days by eating leaves from the trees around he

When she wasn't eating, she was sleeping in the branches.

The forest was the perfect place to live!

Then, one day, a storm announced itself with a **BOOM** of thunder.

Storms were sneaky so Fluffles had to stay alert. It didn't storm often, and the land was very dry. If lightning struck the forest, it could start a fire.

As Fluffles saw the thirsty trees drink up the raindrops, she watched for something else, too. Red and brown clouds in the sky. They were the signs of a fire. Before long...

… the cool grey sky indeed grew red.

Fluffles had to be very fast and very brave.

Koalas have three fingers and two thumbs, so Fluffles was able to shoot up a tree as fast as a rocket.

There, Fluffles waited.

When the fire arrived at Fluffles' tree it jumped at the lower trunk and reached at the branches. Fluffles held on firm, scrunched up her eyes and put all her trust in her paws.

After a time, the fire gave its last hiss. Fluffles knew that she needed to climb down and find friends. But the tree was still too hot! If she climbed down now it might burn her hands.

What was Fluffles going to do?

Fluffles had to be braver than she'd ever been before. It wasn't safe for her in the hot tree.

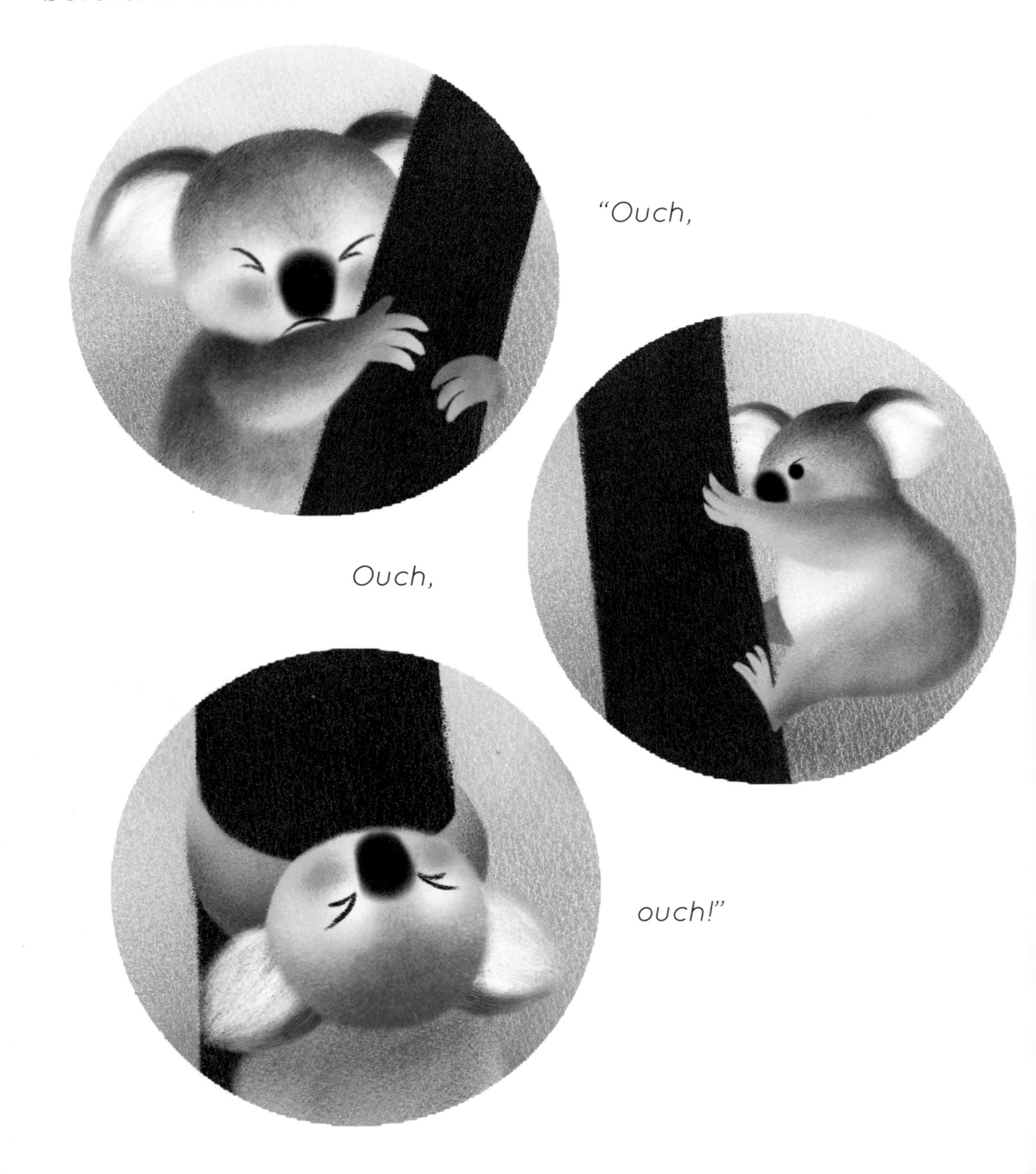

Her paws hurt with every tread. When Fluffles reached the forest floor, her hands were one big **'ouchie'.**

All around, Fluffles could see burned trees. But she could also see helpers.

One of them scooped her up and applied cool cream and special mittens to her sore paws. It felt nice on the outside but didn't soothe her feelings on the inside. Fluffles knew there was only one thing that could do that.

So, when the special mittens were taken off, Fluffles reached out one tender paw until she felt fur just like hers. It felt like home. Familiar smells filled her nose.

Now Fluffles could finally feel better. The big hug erased all worries from the fire and replaced them with relief and comfort. It was a hug so powerful it could have rebuilt the forest.

And when Fluffles and her fellow koalas returned to the forest, slowly but surely, that is just what they did.

One hug at a time.

Did you know this book is based on the real-life story of a koala in Australia?

Australia is home to between 40,000 and 80,000 koalas, who are marsupials. That means when they are babies (joeys), they stay in a cosy pouch on their mum's front while they grow.

Koalas are often seen as a national symbol in Australia. Unfortunately, in recent years, much of the population of koalas has been lost due to drought and bushfires. During the year this story was written, millions of acres burned across Australia, leaving koalas without homes and with injuries.

Fluffles was one of the koalas who was injured in the 2020 bushfires in Adelaide Hills, but volunteers and veterinarians helped Fluffles and her friends by applying special creams and mittens. Most importantly, helpers paired koalas with one another, so they could have a hug. Experts believe koalas feel most comfortable when holding onto something. Fluffles was released back into the wild, along with Drew, Meadows, Rosie, Glen and many more.

How can you help ensure koalas have a safe home? You can support and raise awareness for koala rescue projects and urge law-makers to keep koalas protected.

www.savethekoala.com

First published in 2021 by Frances Lincoln Children's Books,
an imprint of The Quarto Group.
The Old Brewery, 6 Blundell Street, London N7 9BH, United Kingdom.
T (0)20 7700 6700 F (0)20 7700 8066 www.QuartoKnows.com

A catalogue record for this book is available from the British Library.
ISBN 978-0-7112-6157-0
Published by Katie Cotton
Designed by Karissa Santos
Edited by Katy Flint
Production by Nikki Ingram
Manufactured in China CC122020
9 8 7 6 5 4 3 2 1

Photo Credits p29: 1. Sonny Cromelin monitors a koala habitat on September 04, 2020 Photo by Lisa Maree Williams/Getty Images) 2. A female koala recovers in the Native Wildlife Rescue centre on January 29, 2020 (Photo by John Moore/Getty Images) 3. Crisis Response Specialist, Kelly Donithan (R) checks an injured Koala she just rescued, January 15, 2020 (Photo by PETER PARKS/AFP via Getty Images) 4. Koala. (Photo by DeAgostini/Getty Images)

Also in the **True Stories of Animal Heroes** series:

978-0-7112-6143-3

The wolf who found a new way to be a LEADER

Read about Onyx, the wolf pup, who was the scrappy runt of his litter in Yellowstone National Park. Last for food and left out of games, no-one expected much of young Onyx. But as he grew, he took with him a special way of thinking that transformed the underdog into a great leader.

This epic story has a fact section at the back, so you can learn more about wolves and how you can help them.